Sunshine

By Liza Charlesworth

ISBN: 978-1-339-02792-0

Art Director: Tannaz Fassihi; Designer: Tanya Chernyak
Photos © Getty Images and Shutterstock.com.
Copyright © Liza Charlesworth. All rights reserved. Published by Scholastic Inc.

1 2 3 4 5 6 7 8 9 10   68   32 31 30 29 28 27 26 25 24 23

Printed in Jiaxing, China. First printing, August 2023.

SCHOLASTIC

Sunshine is fine!
You can grab a backpack
and take a hike.

If the day is bright,
you can ride on a sailboat.
The wind feels so nice!

You can get a sweet treat.
It's fun to drink a milkshake
or lick a peach ice pop.

When there is sunshine,
you can sit in a treetop.
You can think a lot!

You can grab a playmate
and hop into a sandbox.
You can dig, fill, and sift!

In the sunshine,
you can lie on a haystack.
You have time to daydream.

A DAY IN THE SUNSHINE

Sunshine is fine!
You can hang up snapshots
of the fun things you did.